No Problem

by Lynn Trepicchio
illustrated by Art Alvarez

**Harcourt**

Orlando   Boston   Dallas   Chicago   San Diego

Visit *The Learning Site!*

www.harcourtschool.com

Grandpa can fix anything.
When I showed him my
bicycle, he knew just what
to do.

2

"No problem! We can fix it!"
he said. Then he put me to
work.

The bicycle was just like new!

When a lamp broke, Grandpa
knew just what to do.

"No problem! We can fix it!"
he said. Then I gave him
some tools.

The lamp worked again!

When my little brother
couldn't reach the sink,
Grandpa knew just what to do.

"No problem! We can fix it!"
he said. Then he asked me to
measure some wood.

The little step was just right!

When the water didn't come
out of the faucet, Grandpa
knew just what to do.

"No problem! We can fix it!"
he said. Then he asked me to
turn on the water.

It worked!

When the telephone didn't
work, Grandpa didn't know
what to do.

"No problem! We can fix it!"
I said. I knew just what to
do.

Guess what we did? We fixed
the telephone together!